ATALANTA

THE RACE AGAINST DESTINY

A MYTH

GRAPHIC UNIVERSE™

STORY BY
JUSTINE & RON FONTES

PENCILS AND INKS BY
THOMAS YEATES

EUROPE

N

MEDITERRANEAN SEA

NORTH AFRICA

ATALANTA

THE RACE AGAINST DESTINY

A GREEK MYTH

GREECE

▲ MOUNT OLYMPUS

DELPHI

CALYDON

ATHENS

IONIAN SEA

AEGEAN SEA

GRAPHIC UNIVERSE™

THE ANCIENT GREEK MYTHS THAT TELL OF ATALANTA AND OTHER HEROIC FIGURES DATE BACK MORE THAN TWO THOUSAND YEARS. THE IMAGERY USUALLY ASSOCIATED WITH GREEK MYTHOLOGY IS THAT OF GREECE'S CLASSICAL PERIOD (FROM ABOUT 500 TO 323 BC), COMPLETE WITH GRAND TEMPLES, FLOWING GARMENTS AND MAGNIFICENT STATUES. *ATALANTA: THE RACE AGAINST DESTINY* FOLLOWS THAT TRADITION.

AUTHORS JUSTINE AND RON FONTES RELIED UPON MANY SOURCES, INCLUDING EDITH HAMILTON'S *MYTHOLOGY* AND MICHAEL GRANT'S *MYTHS OF THE GREEKS AND ROMANS*. ARTIST THOMAS YEATES USED HISTORICAL AND TRADITIONAL SOURCES FOR VISUAL DETAILS—FROM IMAGES ON ANCIENT GREEK VASES TO SCULPTURE AND OTHER ARTWORK. DAVID MULROY OF THE UNIVERSITY OF WISCONSIN-MILWAUKEE ENSURED HISTORICAL AND VISUAL ACCURACY.

STORY BY JUSTINE AND RON FONTES

PENCILS AND INKS BY THOMAS YEATES,
WITH SPECIAL THANKS TO TOD SMITH,
KEN HOOPER AND CHRIS MARRINAN

COLOURING BY HI-FI DESIGN

LETTERING BY BILL HAUSER

CONSULTANT: DAVID MULROY,
UNIVERSITY OF WISCONSIN-MILWAUKEE

This book was first published in the USA in 2007. First published in the UK in 2008 by Lerner Books, Dalton House, 60 Windsor Avenue, London SW19 2RR

Website address: www.lernerbooks.co.uk

This edition was updated and edited for UK publication by Discovery Books Ltd., Unit 3, 37 Watling Street, Leintwardine, Shropshire SY7 0LW

British Library Cataloguing in Publication Data

Fontes, Justine
   Atalanta : the race against destiny. - (Graphic myths and legends series)
   1. Atalanta (Greek mythology) - Comic books, strips, etc. - Juvenile fiction 2. Children's stories - Comic books, strips, etc.
   I. Title II. Fontes, Ron III. Yeates, Thomas
741.5

ISBN-13: 978 1 58013 317 3

Printed in China

TABLE OF CONTENTS

ABANDONED

LONG AGO, THE ANCIENT GREEKS BELIEVED IN GODS WHO LIVED ON LOFTY MOUNT OLYMPUS. FROM THEIR CLOUDY PALACE, THESE OLYMPIANS WATCHED MORTAL LIVES UNFOLD LIKE STORIES—AND SOMETIMES THEY INTERFERED IN THESE STORIES. THIS EXPLAINED WHY SOME LIVES RAN STRANGE COURSES.

AND NONE WAS STRANGER THAN THAT OF THE FASTEST WOMAN IN THE WORLD, ATALANTA.

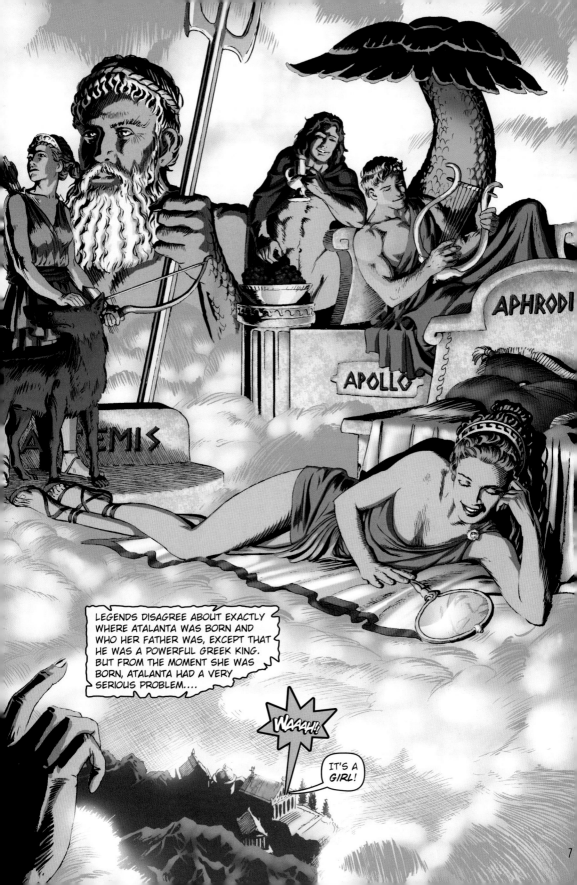

LEGENDS DISAGREE ABOUT EXACTLY WHERE ATALANTA WAS BORN AND WHO HER FATHER WAS, EXCEPT THAT HE WAS A POWERFUL GREEK KING. BUT FROM THE MOMENT SHE WAS BORN, ATALANTA HAD A VERY SERIOUS PROBLEM....

WAAAH!

IT'S A GIRL!

9

SO THE GUARDS TOOK THE NEWBORN FAR FROM THE PALACE.

LET'S GET OUT OF HERE.

WHO *KNOWS* WHAT WILD CREATURES MIGHT BE LURKING ABOUT?

MAY THE *GODS* BE WITH YOU, LITTLE ONE.

WOULD THE SHE-BEAR TEAR ATALANTA TO PIECES?

HAD THE BEAST BEEN SENT BY THE GODS TO PROTECT THE GIRL? HAD ARTEMIS THE GODDESS OF THE WILDERNESS DECIDED TO SPARE ATALANTA SO SHE COULD GROW UP TO BE A FAITHFUL FOLLOWER?

OR WAS IT SIMPLY A MOTHER'S KINDNESS? WHATEVER HER REASON, THE BEAR ADOPTED THE ABANDONED CHILD AS HER OWN.

SHE KEPT THE BABY SAFE AND WARM.

FOUND

ATALANTA SPENT THE NEXT FEW YEARS LIVING LIKE A BEAR CUB.

THEN, ONE DAY, A PARTY OF HUNTERS FOUND THE YOUNG GIRL IN THE FOREST.

THEY TOOK ATALANTA TO LIVE WITH THEM.

MOST OF THE TIME, ATALANTA WAS TOO BUSY HUNTING OR FISHING TO THINK ABOUT THE FUTURE. BUT SOMETIMES SHE WONDERED IF HER LIFE HAD SOME OTHER PURPOSE ...

OTHER GREEK GIRLS KNEW EXACTLY WHAT THEY WERE SUPPOSED TO DO. THEY LEARNED TO SPIN WOOL INTO THREAD, WEAVE WOOL INTO CLOTH, AND SEW CLOTH INTO CLOTHES. IF THEY WERE FORTUNATE, GIRLS LEARNED HOW TO INSTRUCT SERVANTS IN ALL THE TASKS OF HOUSEKEEPING. OTHERWISE, THEY LEARNED TO COOK AND CLEAN. THEY MADE THEIR HAIR LOOK PRETTY, GOT MARRIED, AND BECAME MOTHERS AND GRANDMOTHERS. AS GIRLS, THEY RARELY LEFT THEIR FATHER'S HOUSE. AND AS MARRIED WOMEN, THEY NEARLY ALWAYS STAYED AT HOME, TOO.

14

BUT ATALANTA KNEW NOTHING OF SUCH A LIFE. SHE COULD NOT IMAGINE HERSELF WITH A HUSBAND AND HOUSE.

WHAT AM I SUPPOSED TO DO?

WHY ASK US? WE'RE NOT ORACLES.

WHAT'S AN ORACLE?

SOMEONE WHO SPEAKS FOR THE GODS.

ALL THE GREAT *KINGS* AND *HEROES* ASK ORACLES FOR ADVICE.

THEN I WILL, TOO!

ANSWERS AND ADVENTURES

*T*HERE WERE MANY ORACLES ALL OVER ANCIENT GREECE. OF THESE, THE MOST FAMOUS WAS THE ORACLE OF APOLLO AT DELPHI. AT DELPHI, PRIESTS AND PRIESTESSES ACCEPTED OFFERINGS FROM THOSE WHO SOUGHT ANSWERS FROM THE ORACLE.

ON THE WAY TO CALYDON, ATALANTA WAS IN GOOD COMPANY. MANY OF THOSE WHO FOUGHT THE BOAR WERE FAMOUS HEROES OF LEGEND AND SONG.

JASON LED THE QUEST FOR THE GOLDEN FLEECE ON A GREAT SHIP CALLED THE ARGO.

HIS CREW, CALLED THE ARGONAUTS, INCLUDED SONS OF THE GOD ZEUS HIMSELF: CASTOR THE HORSETAMER AND POLLUX THE BOXING MASTER ...

THESEUS, WHO SLEW THE MONSTER MINOTAUR ...

NESTOR, WHO LIVED TO BE THE OLDEST HERO OF THE TROJAN WAR ...

AND TELAMON, WHO FOUGHT BESIDE THE GREATEST OF ALL GREEK HEROES, HERCULES.

LOOKS LIKE *CASTOR* AND *POLLIX* ARE GOING TO END THIS HUNT RIGHT NOW!

BUT THE BOAR TURNED IN MID-CHARGE AND RACED OFF INTO THE WOODS!

THIS BEAST IS NO MATCH FOR MY SPEED!

THE CREATURE IS *FAST*, TOO!

BUT NOT AS SWIFT AS ATALANTA, I'LL WAGER!

WHEN ATALANTA HAD CAUGHT UP TO THE BOAR, SHE RAISED HER BOW AND SHOT!

SHE LOOKS LIKE A STATUE OF *ARTEMIS!*

OW'! WHO PUT THAT ROOT THERE?

THWACK!

ATALANTA HAS STRUCK FIRST *BLOOD!* ALL HONOUR TO YOUR PROWESS, FAIR *HUNTRESS!*

NOT EXACTLY FATAL. LIKE I SAID, SHE'LL PUT US ALL IN *DANGER.* NOW THE BEAST IS *REALLY* MAD!

LUCKY SHOT.

MISSED! BUT NEXT TIME I'LL...

GOT HIM! BUT HE'S NOT DOWN YET...

MELEAGER'S RAGE WAS SO QUICK AND SO FIERY THAT HIS UNCLES WERE DEAD BEFORE HE KNEW WHAT HAD HAPPENED.

BY THE GODS, MELEAGER—WHAT HAVE YOU DONE?

I...I DON'T KNOW WHAT CAME OVER ME.

OH, NO! TWO MURDERS ON MY ACCOUNT! WAS I WRONG TO COME HERE? AM I CURSED?

GO TO THE PALACE. TELL THEM THE NEWS!

QUEEN ALTHEA, SOMETHING HORRIBLE HAS HAPPENED!

I'M SORRY, MY QUEEN. HIS BLOOD STILL HOT FROM THE HUNT, MELEAGER STRUCK WITH SUCH SPEED THAT NO ONE COULD STOP HIM.

NO! IT CANNOT BE!

OH, HOW CRUEL THE FATES CAN BE! BUT NOW THERE IS ONLY ONE THING TO DO—HOWEVER AWFUL.

YEARS AGO, WHEN HER SON WAS JUST ONE WEEK OLD, ALTHEA HAD SEEN THE THREE FATES SPINNING THE THREAD OF MELEAGER'S LIFE. THE FATES DETERMINED EVERY MORTAL'S DESTINY.

WHEN THIS LOG BURNS OUT, THE SPAN OF HIS LIFE WILL BE ENDED.

POOR, *UNFORTUNATE* BABE.

SO IT WILL BE. WE DO NOT DECIDE.

WE ONLY SERVE THE NATURAL ORDER. ONCE A MORTAL'S COURSE IS SET, IT CANNOT BE CHANGED.

MELEAGER! I CANNOT LET OUR *SON* DIE SO YOUNG!

IF THIS LOG NEVER BURNS OUT, MY CHILD WILL *LIVE!*

ALTHEA HAD KEPT THE LOG HIDDEN FOR YEARS. BUT NOW THAT HER SON WAS A MURDERER ...

CAN I *CHEAT DESTINY* SO EASILY?

TO AVENGE MY *BROTHERS,* I MUST KILL MY *SON!*

AT THAT VERY MOMENT ON THE HUNTING GROUNDS, HORRIBLE PAINS BURNED THROUGH MELEAGER'S BODY.

RRRGH!!

IN MOMENTS, THE LOG HAD BURNED TO ASH—AND MELEAGER WAS *DEAD...*

...AND ATALANTA WAS LEFT TO PONDER THE CRUEL MYSTERIES OF THE GODS.

27

A CALL WENT OUT ACROSS THE LAND, ANNOUNCING AN UNUSUAL CHANCE TO WIN THE HAND OF ATALANTA. MANY SUITORS, EAGER TO HAVE SUCH A LOVELY AND FAMOUS BRIDE, FLOCKED TO THE KING'S PALACE. BUT THEY HAD LITTLE IDEA WHAT THEY WERE GETTING INTO.

I WILL MARRY NO MAN WHO CANNOT BEAT ME IN A RACE.

I'D RUN AROUND THE WORLD FOR HER HAND!

WITH ATALANTA THE PRIZE, I'LL RUN FASTER THAN THE WIND!

NOW I WISH I HAD CHOSEN SPRINTING INSTEAD OF WRESTLING.

MANY OF GREECE'S FINEST AND FASTEST WERE EAGER TO TRY.

THIS OUGHT TO DISCOURAGE THEM—AND SPARE MY FEET.

WIN THE RACE AND I WILL BE YOUR WIFE. LOSE IT—AND YOU WILL LOSE YOUR LIFE!

EVERYONE KNEW HOW FAST ATALANTA WAS. BUT SOME STILL CHOSE TO RUN THE DEADLY RACE.

MY LIFE IS NOTHING WITHOUT ATALANTA!

TO LOSE ATALANTA WOULD BE BAD ENOUGH. BUT...

I'D RATHER DIE THAN NOT MARRY ATALANTA!

I SUPPOSE I CAN FIND A SLOWER WIFE.

3

BEFORE THE RACE, HIPPOMENES WENT TO A TEMPLE OF APHRODITE.

O, *APHRODITE!* FAVOUR ME WITH VICTORY—AND WITH ATALANTA'S *LOVE!*

LOOK, *EROS,* MY SON! LOVE BRINGS ANOTHER PROUD MAN BEGGING FOR FAVOURS.

THEY ALL FALL IN THE END. WHAT IS THIS ONE'S NAME?

HIPPOMENES. HE PRAYS FOR HELP IN COURTING *ATALANTA.*

THE WORLD'S FASTEST WOMAN? SHE'S QUITE THE *BEAUTY!*

YES, SO I'VE HEARD. BUT THAT DOESN'T PUT HER ABOVE LOVE.

SHALL I NOTCH AN ARROW TO WIN HER HEART FOR HIM?

THAT MAY NOT BE NECESSARY. I'LL VISIT HANDSOME HIPPOMENES AND SEE WHAT I CAN DO.

'AT THE WEST OF THE WORLD, WHERE THE SUN SETS, IS THE GARDEN OF HESPERIDES, PLANTED BY THE ANCIENTS. IN IT GROWS A *GOLDEN APPLE TREE,* GUARDED BY A SLEEPLESS DRAGON. THESE APPLES COME FROM THAT TREE. TOSS THEM DURING THE RACE, AND ATALANTA WILL NOT BE ABLE TO RESIST THEIR BEAUTY. SHE WILL *HAVE* TO STOP TO PICK THEM UP.'

APHRODITE!!

'THANK YOU, GODDESS!'

THE GODDESS SOON UNDERSTOOD THE YOUNG LOVER'S PROBLEM. FORTUNATELY, SHE KNEW JUST WHAT TO DO.

DESIRE WILL DISTRACT YOUR QUICK PREY. NO MORTAL CAN RESIST THESE APPLES.

NO WONDER! THEY'RE SO DIVINELY *BEAUTIFUL!*

35

IT WAS TOO LATE TO STOP THE RACE. AND ATALANTA STILL WAS NOT SURE WHETHER SHE WANTED TO WIN OR LOSE.

I THINK...I THINK I *LOVE* HIM! BUT WHAT ABOUT THE ORACLE?

DO YOU SEE HOW SHE LOOKS AT HIM? MAYBE ATALANTA HAS MET HER MATCH.

ONLY IF HE CAN OUTRUN HER!

ATALANTA RAN SO FAST THAT HIPPOMENES WAS BEHIND ALMOST BEFORE HE BEGAN.

HOW DID SHE GET SO FAR AHEAD ALREADY? I ONLY HOPE APHRODITE'S TRICK WILL WORK...

BEFORE LONG HIPPOMENES TOSSED THE FIRST APPLE.

Gasp!!

I *MUST* HAVE THAT APPLE!

AS ATALANTA STOPPED TO PICK UP THE APPLE, HIPPOMENES RACED AHEAD.

A BRIDE AFTER ALL

AFTER THE PROPER RITES AND SACRIFICES, ATALANTA AND HIPPOMENES WERE MARRIED.

MAYBE THE ORACLE WAS **WRONG**. OR THE PRIESTS MIXED UP WHAT SHE SAID. MAYBE I CAN BE **HAPPILY MARRIED** AFTER ALL!

I'M SO LUCKY TO HAVE ATALANTA! THE GODS HAVE TRULY SMILED ON ME. BUT I CAN'T SHAKE THE FEELING THAT I'VE **FORGOTTEN** SOMETHING...

AS THE BRIDE'S FATHER, THE KING HOSTED A LARGE, LAVISH BANQUET. ON SPECIAL OCCASIONS LIKE WEDDINGS, GREEK WOMEN LEFT THE SAFETY OF THEIR HOMES. BUT THEY SAT AT SEPARATE TABLES FROM THE MEN.

TO MY BOLD AND BEAUTIFUL **DAUGHTER**, AND MY HANDSOME AND CLEVER SON-IN-LAW.

MAY **HERA** BLESS THEM WITH A HAPPY UNION AND MANY HEALTHY **SONS!**

TO MY NEW FATHER-IN-LAW AND THE FINE TABLE HE SETS!

BUT HIGH ABOVE ON MOUNT OLYMPUS, A CERTAIN GODDESS WAITED FOR SOME WORDS SHE DID NOT HEAR.

THE ANGRY GODDESS SOON ARRANGED HER REVENGE. ONE PEACEFUL DAY WHEN THE NEWLYWEDS WERE STROLLING BLISSFULLY THROUGH THE FOREST...

...THEY SPOTTED AN OLD CAVE.

ARE YOU *TIRED*, MY LOVE?

Yawn! YES...I SUPPOSE WE *HAVE* WALKED A LONG WAY.

LET'S REST FOR A FEW MOMENTS THERE, IN THAT CAVE.

WHAT A *STRANGE* PLACE!

THIS IS NO ORDINARY CAVE.

I THINK IT'S A *TEMPLE.* WE SHOULDN'T BE HERE.

YOU'RE NOT *SCARED*, ARE YOU?

I'M NEVER SCARED!

THAT'S WHY I MARRIED YOU!

RHEA CURSED THE UNFORTUNATE COUPLE. SUDDENLY...

GLOSSARY

APHRODITE: the Greek goddess of love

APOLLO: the Greek god of music, poetry, prophecy and light. Apollo is the twin brother of Artemis.

ARTEMIS: the Greek goddess of hunting and the wilderness, as well as of childbirth. She is Apollo's twin sister.

ATALANTA: the great huntress of ancient Greece. Atalanta was also a great athlete.

ATHENA: the Greek goddess of wisdom

CALYDON: a city in central Greece where Atalanta and many Greek heroes fought the Calydonian boar

DELPHI: a city in central Greece where the oracle of the god Apollo is located

EROS: Aphrodite's son and the god of love

FATES: the three goddesses who oversee human fate. Clotho spins the thread that represents a person's life, Lachesis measures it and Atropos cuts it with her scissors.

HERA: the Greek goddess of marriage and childbirth who is married to Zeus

HIPPOMENES: Atalanta's suitor. During the race for her hand, he tricks her with the golden apples and wins the race against her, after which they are married.

MELEAGER: the son of King Oeneus of Calydon

MOUNT OLYMPUS: the home of the Greek gods and goddesses

ORACLE: in ancient Greece, a priestess or other person through whom the gods were believed to communicate

RHEA: the mother of Zeus and other major gods

ZEUS: the highest Greek god and the ruler of Mount Olympus

FURTHER READING, WEBSITE AND FILMS

Blyton, Enid. *Tales of Ancient Greece* (Myths and Legends) Element Books Ltd, 1998. An inspirational collection of stories of love, treachery, foolishness, tragedy and humour. All the famous stories are here from the foolish tales of Phaeton and the Sun-Horses and Icarus and his wings, to the sorrowful fate of Orpheus and Eurydice.

Clash of the Titans. DVD. Directed by Desmond Davis. Warner Home Video, 1981. Rereleased 2004. Although this movie does not tell Atalanta's story, it does feature Aphrodite, Zeus and other gods who affected her fate. It describes the hero Perseus and his quest to kill the Gorgon Medusa.

Encyclopedia of Greek Mythology: Atalanta.
http://www.mythweb.com/encyc/entries/atalanta.html
With engaging cartoons and easy-to-read text, this child-friendly site explores the story of Atalanta and also of many other Greek heroes and heroines.

Wilkinson, Philip and Neil Philip. *Mythology* (Eyewitness Companions). Dorling Kindersley Publishers Ltd, 2007. World myths, gods, heroes, creatures and mythical places are revealed.

Yole, Jane and Robert J Harris. *Atalanta and the Arcadian Beast* (Young Heroes) HarperCollins Publishers, 2003. The story of Atalanta's upbringing and her quest to slay the beast that terrorises the Arcadian countryside.

CREATING *ATALANTA: THE RACE AGAINST DESTINY*

In creating the story, authors Justine and Ron Fontes drew upon many resources, including Edith Hamilton's classic *Mythology* and the widely respected *Myths of the Greeks and Romans* by professor and classics scholar Michael Grant. Artist Thomas Yeates used historical and traditional sources to shape the story's visual details—from images on ancient Greek vases to sculpture and other artwork. David Mulroy of the University of Wisconsin-Milwaukee ensured the accuracy of the story's historical and visual details. Together, the text and the art bring to life this story from ancient Greece.

POLLEX

JASON

TELAMON

original pencil sketch from page 21

CASTOR

INDEX

ABOUT THE AUTHORS AND THE ARTIST

RON AND JUSTINE FONTES met at a publishing house in New York City, USA. Ron worked for the comic book department and Justine was an editorial assistant in children's books. Together they have written nearly 500 children's books, in every format from board books to historical novels. From their home in Maine, the Fonteses publish *critter news*, a strictly-for-fun newsletter. They also launched Sonic Comics with their first graphic novel *Tales of the Terminal Diner*, a unique anthology with continuing characters. Other published projects include *The Trojan Horse: The Fall of Troy, Demeter & Persephone: Spring Held Hostage* and *The Wooden Sword*. Life-long library lovers, the Fonteses long to write 1,001 books before retiring to read.

THOMAS YEATES began his art training in high school and continued at Utah State University and Sacramento State in the USA. Subsequently, he was a member of the first class at Joe Kubert's School, a trade course for aspiring comic book artists in New Jersey. Yeates has worked as an illustrator for DC Comics, Marvel, Dark Horse and many other companies, drawing Tarzan, Zorro, the Swamp Thing, Timespirits, Captain America and Conan. For the Graphic Myths and Legends series, he illustrated *King Arthur: Excalibur Unsheathed* and *Robin Hood: Outlaw of Sherwood Forest*. Yeates lives in northern California with his wife and daughter.